Level 2

Rainforest Boy

Retold by Rachel Bladon
Illustrated by Lorena Alvarez

Contents

Rainforest Boy   2

Exercises   20

Picture Dictionary   22

About *Classic Tales*   24

OXFORD
UNIVERSITY PRESS

These children live near the rainforest. They want to play. They want to play with their friend Curupira, the Rainforest Boy.

'Curupira!' they say. 'Curupira!'

Here's Curupira! Curupira is the Rainforest Boy. He lives in the rainforest and he loves the animals and the trees.

Curupira has red hair and strange feet. His feet are backwards! He is strong and very fast, and he can whistle very loud.

The rainforest is very big. But the children are safe with Curupira. The animals and trees are safe too. Curupira is their friend.

'Come with me!' says Curupira to the children. 'Come and see something.'

The children go into the rainforest with Curupira. They walk next to the river, and up a hill. Then they come to a big tree.

Come with me!

'Look!' says Curupira quietly. 'Look at the jaguar with her cubs!'

And there, under the tree, are three little cubs, with their mother.

'Oh!' say the children. 'Look at them!'

Look!

'Sometimes bad men come and they kill the jaguars,' says Curupira. 'They want their beautiful coats. We must stop the bad men. We must help the jaguars, so they are safe. Then the cubs can get big and strong. One day they can have cubs too.'

'Please help them, Curupira,' says a little girl.

The children follow Curupira out of the rainforest. Then they say goodbye, and run home.

'Goodbye!' Curupira says. 'Come back tomorrow! Come and see the jaguars tomorrow!'

But a man is listening.
A man with a gun.
A hunter.

'I can kill those jaguars and get their coats,' thinks the hunter. 'I can come back tomorrow with my friends, and we can follow that boy. He can take us to the jaguars.'

But Curupira sees the hunter.

I can kill those jaguars.

The next day the children come back. The hunter comes back too. He comes back with his friends.

'Curupira!' the children say. 'Let's go and see the jaguars!'

'Not today, my friends,' says Curupira. 'The jaguars are tired. You cannot come with me today. But come back tomorrow.'

Let's go and see the jaguars!

Not today, my friends.

The children go home, and Curupira goes into the rainforest. He doesn't walk next to the river. He doesn't walk up the hill. He doesn't go to the jaguars.

Curupira goes up some rocks and behind some trees. He goes up hills and down hills. He walks and walks.

The hunters follow Curupira, and Curupira knows it.

All morning Curupira walks. He walks, and the men follow. The men are tired. They are hot and hungry.

'Where are the jaguars?' they think.

Where is he?

Suddenly Curupira runs. He runs very, very fast, and the hunters can't follow him.

'Where is he?' they say. 'We can't see him!'

The hunters come to a big tree. They cannot see Curupira. They are hot and tired, and hungry, too. They want to find the jaguars.

Then one of the hunters says, 'Look! His footprints! We can follow his footprints. They can take us to the jaguars.'

Look! His footprints!

Curupira is up the tree. He laughs quietly. They are his footprints, but they are backwards footprints. They don't go to the jaguars.

They go down hills and up hills. Then they go out of the rainforest!

The hunters follow the footprints. They are tired and hungry.

'Where are these footprints going?' they ask. 'Where is that boy? And where are the jaguars?'

Where are these footprints going?

Then the hunters hear a whistle – a loud, loud whistle.

'What's that?' they say. 'Is it an animal?'

Now they are afraid, too. They are tired, hungry, and afraid.

'Where are we?' they say. But they don't know, so they follow the footprints.

All afternoon, the hunters follow the footprints. They hear another whistle, and they are afraid.

'There are strange things in this rainforest!' they say.

It is evening now, and they want to go home.

'These footprints aren't taking us to the jaguars,' they say. 'But can they take us out of the rainforest?'

The men follow the footprints … and at last they come out of the rainforest.

'I'm afraid!' says one of the hunters. 'I don't want to come back here.'

'No!' say the others. 'Let's go home!'

And they run home.

Curupira is in a tree. He sees the men, and he laughs and laughs.

I don't want to come back here!

I help the rainforest.

The next day the children come back.

'Can we see the jaguars today, Curupira?' they ask.

'Yes, you can see the jaguars today!' he says. 'The jaguars are not tired today.'

'Are you helping them, Curupira?' asks the little girl.

'Yes,' says Curupira. 'I always help the jaguars. I help the rainforest and all the rainforest animals, so they are safe.'

1 Write the words.

under   down   out of   next to   ~~up~~   behind

__up__ the hill

_____ the tree

_____ the rocks

_____ the river

_____ the rainforest

_____ the hill

2 Write the words.

1 This is _Curupira_ .

2 He has _____ hair.

3 His feet are _____ .

4 He is strong and very _____ .

5 He can _____ very loud.

3 Number the sentences 1–7. Then write sentence 8.

- ☐ The hunters follow Curupira.
- 1 The children go and see the jaguars with Curupira.
- ☐ Curupira runs very fast, and the hunters can't follow him.
- ☐ The children come back and say, 'Can we see the jaguars today?'
- ☐ The hunters follow Curupira's footprints.
- ☐ The hunters run home.
- ☐ A hunter listens to Curupira and the children.
- 8 The next day _____

4 What do they say? Write the words.

1 Look at the jaguar <u>with her cubs</u>!

2 Come back _____!

3 Look! _____!

4 Is it _____?

WHISTLE...

Picture Dictionary

afraid *He's afraid.*

follow

backwards

footprints

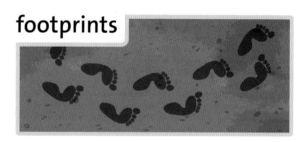

coat

gun

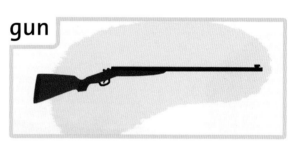

come back

hill

cubs

hunter

jaguars

river

kill

rocks

loud

safe

next to *next to the river*

strong *He's strong.*

out of *out of the rainforest*

tree

rainforest

whistle

Classic Tales

Classic stories retold for learners of English — bringing the magic of traditional storytelling to the language classroom

For Classic Tales Teacher's Handbook, visit www.oup.com/elt/readers/classictales

Level 1: 100 headwords
- The Enormous Turnip
- The Lazy Grasshopper
- The Little Red Hen
- Lownu Mends the Sky
- The Magic Cooking Pot
- The Magpie and the Milk
- Mansour and the Donkey
- Peach Boy
- The Princess and the Pea
- Rumpelstiltskin
- The Shoemaker and the Elves
- Three Billy-Goats

Level 2: 150 headwords
- Amrita and the Trees
- Big Baby Finn
- The Fisherman and his Wife
- The Gingerbread Man
- Jack and the Beanstalk
- King Arthur and the Sword
- Rainforest Boy
- Thumbelina
- The Town Mouse and the Country Mouse
- The Ugly Duckling

Level 3: 200 headwords
- Aladdin
- Bambi and the Prince of the Forest
- Goldilocks and the Three Bears
- The Heron and the Hummingbird
- The Little Mermaid
- Little Red Riding Hood
- Rapunzel

Level 4: 300 headwords
- Cinderella
- Don Quixote: Adventures of a Spanish Knight
- The Goose Girl
- Sleeping Beauty
- The Twelve Dancing Princesses

Level 5: 400 headwords
- Beauty and the Beast
- The Magic Brocade
- Pinocchio
- Snow White and the Seven Dwarfs

OXFORD
UNIVERSITY PRESS

Great Clarendon Street, Oxford, OX2 6DP, United Kingdom

Oxford University Press is a department of the University of Oxford. It furthers the University's objective of excellence in research, scholarship, and education by publishing worldwide. Oxford is a registered trade mark of Oxford University Press in the UK and in certain other countries

© Oxford University Press 2014

The moral rights of the author have been asserted

First published in 2014

2023

13

No unauthorized photocopying

ISBN: 978 0 19 423980 6   Book
ISBN: 978 0 19 410821 8   e-Book
ISBN: 978 0 19 423986 8   Activity Book and Play
ISBN: 978 0 19 401406 9   Audio Pack

Printed in China

This book is printed on paper from certified and well-managed sources

ACKNOWLEDGEMENTS

Illustrations by: Lorena Alvarez / Bright Agency